BIBLE STORIES

The Flood

Written by

Alain Royer and Georges Carpentier

Illustrated by

Sylvie Montmoulineix

Heinemann

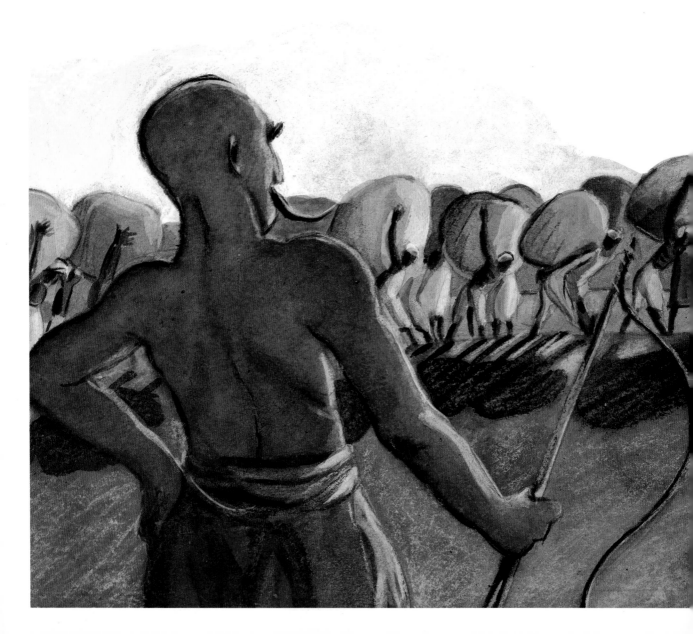

There were many people on the earth.
God saw that they were getting more and
more wicked.

And so God said, 'I shall wipe the earth clean. I shall wipe all of the people and animals off the earth. I shall even clear the birds out of the sky. I am sorry that I ever made them.'

But God saw that Noah was a good man, so he wanted to save him. God said to him, 'Build an ark, a large ship.'

God said, 'Get in to the ark, you, your wife, your three sons and their wives. And take on board one male and one female of each animal that lives on earth.'

Noah did as God told him. And God made it rain on the earth for forty days and forty nights. The water rose and covered everything, even the mountains. All the people and all the animals died.

There was no one left, except Noah and those who were with him on the ark. The water covered the earth for one hundred and fifty days.

God remembered Noah and made the rain stop, and the water go down. The ark came to rest on the top of Mount Ararat.

Noah opened a window and sent a dove into the sky. In the evening, the bird came back. It carried an olive twig in its beak. Noah then knew that the water no longer covered the whole earth, because somewhere the bird had found an olive tree.

Soon the earth dried. God said to Noah, 'Come out of the ark, you, your wife, your sons and your sons' wives.'

And God added, 'Let the birds and animals, and all the little creatures that creep upon the ground also come out. Let them multiply and fill the earth with their children.'

Noah did as God told him and offered him a sacrifice. God was pleased with Noah and thought, 'I will let them live and fill the earth with their children.'

God blessed Noah and his sons and said to them, 'I shall be your friend and the friend of your children, and of your children's children. The rainbow will be the sign of this promise to you and the people and animals that live on earth. Never again will there be a flood to end all life.'